Einojuhani

Rautavaara

Summer Thoughts

Violin & piano

Boosey & Hawkes Music Publishers Ltd
www.boosey.com

Published by Boosey & Hawkes Music Publishers Ltd
Aldwych House
71–91 Aldwych
London
WC2B 4HN

www.boosey.com

an  company

ISMN 979-0-060-12041-1

Printed in Germany by WEGA-Verlag, GmbH, Mainz

SUMMER THOUGHTS

EINOJUHANI RAUTAVAARA
(b 1928)